MARVEL

© 2017 MARVEL

Marvel Heroes Annual 2018 is published by Panini Publishing, a division of Panini UK Limited. Office of publication: Panini UK Ltd. Brockbourne House, 77 Mount Ephraim, Tunbridge Wells, Kent, TN4 8BS. MARVEL, and all related characters: TM & © 2017 Marvel Entertainment, LLC and its subsidiaries. Licensed by Marvel Characters B.V. www.marvel.com. All rights reserved. No similarity between any of the names, characters, persons and/or institutions in this edition with those of any living or dead person or institution is intended, and any such similarity which may exist is purely coincidental. This publication may not be sold, except by authorised dealers, and is sold subject to the condition that it shall not be sold or distributed with any part of its cover or markings removed, nor in a mutilated condition. This publication is produced under licence from Marvel Characters, Inc. through Panini S.p.A. Printed in Italy. ISBN: 978-1-84653-230-6

© 2017 MARVEL

FSC
www.fsc.org
MIX
Paper from
responsible sources
FSC® C005461

£7.99

AVENGERS

MIGHTY MARVEL FUN

It's time for Thor to prove his worthiness! Odin's staged a maze for the God of Thunder... Help him complete the Labyrinth of Honour!

START

MUSPELHEIM

FROM WHICH REALM DOES SURTUR COME FROM?

DUSSELDORF

THE DESTROYER NEEDS A SOUL WITHIN THE ARMOUR TO CONTROL IT.

TRUE

FALSE

THE MIGHTY HAMMER, MJOLNIR WAS FORGED FROM WHICH MATERIAL?

VIBRANIUM

THE HEART OF A STAR

DIFFICULTY LEVEL!

TRUE OR FALSE?

TICK THE BOXES TO SHOW WHETHER YOU THINK THESE 'FACTS' ABOUT THE ENEMIES IN THE COMIC STRIP ARE TRUE OR FALSE!

1. Doc Ock used to work for the Green Goblin's human persona - Norman Osborn - at his company, Oscorp.

TRUE ✓
FALSE ✓

2. The Green Goblin has no superhuman powers, just his arsenal of machines and weapons.

TRUE ✓
FALSE ✓

3. Kraven's real name is Kristoff Pavlova.

TRUE ✓
FALSE ✓

4. Even if Sandman's grains are scattered miles apart, he is able to reform back to his original shape.

TRUE ✓
FALSE ✓

5. Doc Ock created the Venom symbiote from Spider-Man's DNA.

TRUE ✓
FALSE ✓

6. Kraven considers himself the world's second-best hunter!

TRUE ✓
FALSE ✓

ANSWERS ON PAGE 61

TO TURN THE TIDE

JOE CARAMAGNA-WRITER   RON LIM-PENCILER   SCOTT HANNA-INKER   CARLOS LOPEZ-COLORIST
VC's JC-LETTERER   MARK BASSO-ASSISTANT EDITOR   BILL ROSEMANN-EDITOR
AXEL ALONSO-EDITOR IN CHIEF   JOE QUESADA-CHIEF CREATIVE OFFICER   DAN BUCKLEY-PUBLISHER   ALAN FINE-EXEC. PRODUCER

CONTINUED ON PAGE 22!

MONSTEI

The planet's oceans are full of untold mysteries – not to mention a heck of a lot of baddies to boot! Check out our rundown of other underwater enemies who love causing trouble for Earth's mightiest heroes!

SLUJ

This 60 foot tall hulking mass of rubbish and toxic waste started life as a failed lab experiment. After being flushed into the ocean, it merged with all the rubbish and sewage from New York City and grew into a huge, seriously stinky monster! Sluj was eventually taken down by a gene-scrambling virus, but not before it had covered New York City in a thick layer of putrid slime!

POWERGRID	1	2	3	4	5	6	7
INTELLIGENCE							
STRENGTH							
SPEED							
DURABILITY							
ENERGY PROJECTION							
FIGHTING SKILLS							

POWERGRID	1	2	3	4	5	6	7
INTELLIGENCE							
STRENGTH							
SPEED							
DURABILITY							
ENERGY PROJECTION							
FIGHTING SKILLS							

TIGER SHARK

Once an Olympic swimmer, Todd Arliss underwent an experimental procedure that spliced his genes with those of an Atlantean and a tiger shark. Now he possesses superhuman strength and stamina, as long as he is in contact with water. Because of this he wears a special suit that constantly bathes his body in a thin layer of water.

KRANG

An angry Atlantean with a major mistrust of surface-dwellers, Krang is a former military general who used to command a vast underwater army. Along with trying to seize the throne of Atlantis, he has terrorised the surface world numerous times, clashing with the likes of Captain America and Iron Man.

POWERGRID	1	2	3	4	5	6	7
INTELLIGENCE	■	■	■				
STRENGTH	■	■	■	■			
SPEED	■	■	■	■			
DURABILITY	■	■	■				
ENERGY PROJECTION	■	■	■				
FIGHTING SKILLS	■	■					

GIGANTO

Ever wondered what a blue whale would look like if it had arms, legs and a really bad attitude? Just take a look at these guys to find out! Normally found slumbering on the ocean floor, they can be only be awoken by an Atlantean artefact called the Horn of Proteus. Whoever blows it can also use the horn to command these vast creatures to do their bidding!

POWERGRID	1	2	3	4	5	6	7
INTELLIGENCE	■						
STRENGTH	■	■	■	■	■	■	
SPEED	■	■					
DURABILITY	■	■	■	■			
ENERGY PROJECTION	■						
FIGHTING SKILLS	■						

ASK A VILLAIN!

ATTUMA ANSWERS YOUR LETTERS!

Why do you wear that silly gold hat? Don't you bump your head every time you go through a door?

Dolph Fin

Do not DARE to insult my magnificent golden headwear, human worm! It is of significant cultural importance to my people and should be respected as such. Also, it successfully covers Attuma's bald spot.

When I'm in the bath my skin goes all wrinkly. You live in the sea so your skin must be wrinkly all the time, right?

Carol Reef

What?! You DARE compare your puny human skin to my own? Of course I don't wrinkle. Attuma is smooth, supple and extra strong, like the hide of a mighty whale. Also, Attuma has a very good Atlantean beautician who makes an excellent sea cucumber and squid ink skin cream.

Isn't the sea full of scary creatures like sharks? What about jellyfish? I heard some of them can sting you real bad.

Anne Chovy

Sharks? BAH! There is nothing, NOTHING in the sea more fearsome than the great Attuma! And as for jellyfish... I EAT JELLYFISH FOR BREAKFAST! Normally on toast with a few fillets of cod or lightly grilled with a small seaweed salad.

Why are you always so moody?

John Dory

I'm not moo— wait... are you insulting me? FEEBLE MINDED HUMANS! ATTUMA WILL NOT STAND FOR THIS MOCKERY A SECOND LONGER! THAT IS ENOUGH OF YOUR FOOLISH QUESTIONS!!!

BAN

Doctor Bruce Banner has always struggled to contain his alter ego - The Hulk! He needs your help in the laboratory to better understand his unique condition. Are you up to the task?

1.

ATOMIC POWER

Which one of these atoms is gamma charged? Find the path which leads to the green one...

DIFFICULTY LEVEL

2. THE CALMING SERUM

Help Banner locate the prototype on the system.
Quick - before the Hulk in him starts to get angry!

A. **B.** **C.**

D. **E.** **F.**

HULK'S SERUM IS:

Made with gamma rays.

NOT a light colour.

A bubbly liquid

water-based.

ANSWER

3. GAMMA CODING

Now enter the special code that will regulate Bruce Banner's gamma levels. Draw a line that flows through the correct sequence:

START

FINISH

CORRECT SEQUENCE

DRACULA HAS TRICKED YOUR MIND INTO SEEING THINGS DIFFERENTLY! CATCH HIM OUT BY DETECTING THE 8 CHANGES HE CAUSED IN THE IMAGE BELOW!

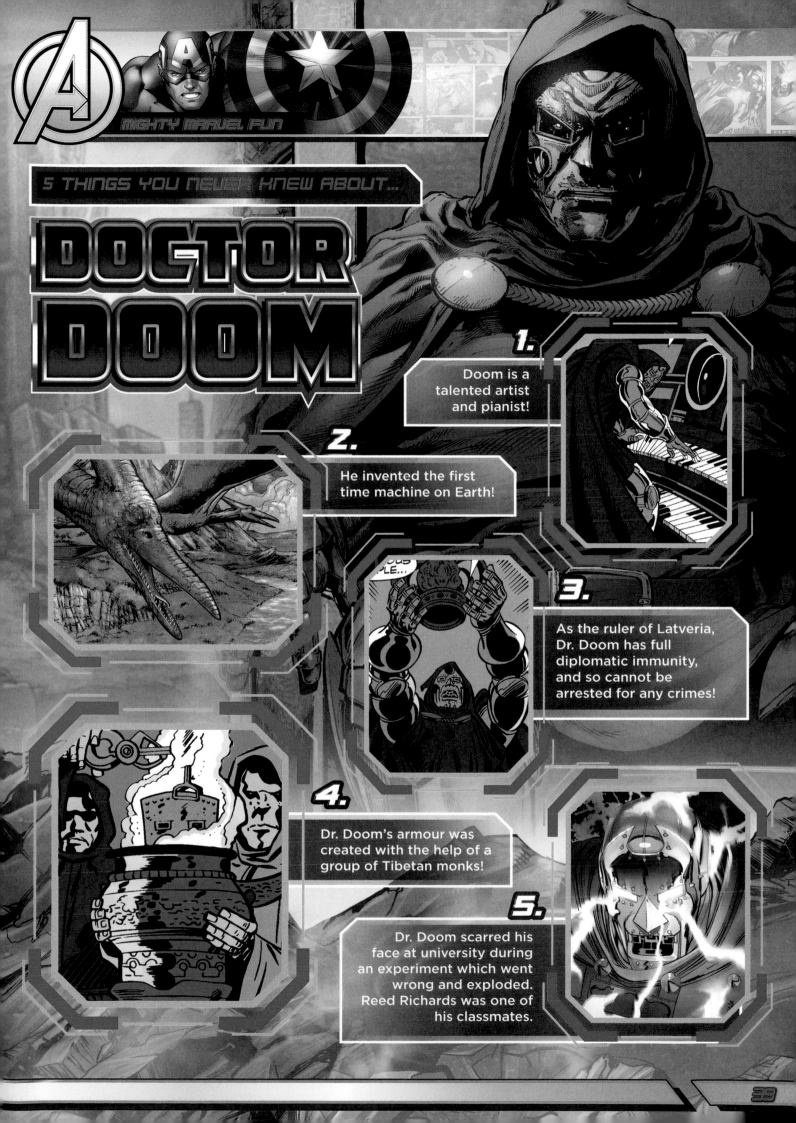

5 THINGS YOU NEVER KNEW ABOUT...

DOCTOR DOOM

1.
Doom is a talented artist and pianist!

2.
He invented the first time machine on Earth!

3.
As the ruler of Latveria, Dr. Doom has full diplomatic immunity, and so cannot be arrested for any crimes!

4.
Dr. Doom's armour was created with the help of a group of Tibetan monks!

5.
Dr. Doom scarred his face at university during an experiment which went wrong and exploded. Reed Richards was one of his classmates.

EVERY HERO AND VILLAIN NEEDS A PLACE TO UNWIND, TO PLAN, OR TO PLOT. AND TODAY WE ARE GOING TO TAKE A LOOK AT SOME OF THE COOLEST SECRET HQS IN THE MIGHTY MARVEL UNIVERSE!

S.H.I.E.L.D. HELICARRIER

What makes the S.H.I.E.L.D. Helicarrier so cool is that there are several of them... so if one gets compromised there's always another ready to take its place.

HISTORY:

TONY STARK

Created by... you guessed it; Tony Stark, the Helicarrier is ideal for a swift response anywhere it is needed.

SECURITY AND ARMAMENTS:

Aircraft, highly trained agents, helicopters.

3 SECRECY FACTOR

4 POWER FACTOR

4 TECH FACTOR

ET BASES!

AVENGERS TOWER

Okay, so Avengers Tower isn't particularly secret but it's still one of the greatest headquarters ever!

HISTORY:

Avengers Tower is the main tower of the Stark Tower Complex in Midtown Manhattan. Tony Stark donated the top three floors of this pad to the Avengers after their original HQ Avengers Mansion was destroyed.

SECURITY AND ARMAMENTS:

The Tower is protected by its very own residents: Earth's mightiest heroes, the Avengers!

0	5	5
SECRECY FACTOR	POWER FACTOR	TECH FACTOR

CASTLE DRACULA

This place is by far the creepiest hideout ever. Nowhere else has chills and atmosphere like here!

HISTORY:

Built in the Carpathian Mountains of Transylvania, the castle has been invaded many times but always withstands any threats.

DRACULA

SECURITY AND ARMAMENTS:

Enter at your own peril – a vast army of the undead, black magic and hungry wolves await you!

4 SECRECY FACTOR
5 POWER FACTOR
1 TECH FACTOR

HYDRA SKY FORTRESS

HYDRA have got more secret hideouts than any other organisation, but this sky base is easily the most impressive and the hardest to find!

SECURITY AND ARMAMENTS:

Heavily armed with deadly weaponry. If you want to take out a HYDRA HQ make sure you are fuiiy prepared!

5 SECRECY FACTOR
3 POWER FACTOR
3 TECH FACTOR

CASTLE DOOM

Castle Doom might seem kind of old school as far as secret HQs go, but don't be fooled, Doctor Doom's lair comes with all mod-cons!

DOCTOR DOOM

HISTORY:

This 110 room castle overlooks Doomstadt, the capital of Doctor Doom's Kingdom of Latveria. It was built in the 16th century and is the centre of the Latverian government.

SECURITY AND ARMAMENTS:

Guarded by Doom-bots, Latverian guards, and force fields.

1	5	4
SECRECY FACTOR	POWER FACTOR	TECH FACTOR

S.H.I.E.L.D. ALERT S.H.I.E.L.D. ALERT S.H.I.E.L.D. ALERT S.H.I.E

S.H.I.E.L.D. NEEDS YOUR HELP. ONE OF OUR AGENTS HAS GONE MISSING IN ONE OF THESE SECRET HQS. LOOK AT THE CLUES FROM HIS RECENT REPORTS AND COMPARE THEM WITH THE DATA FILES TO SEE IF YOU CAN FIND THE AGENT'S LOCATION.

1. THE SECRET HEADQUARTERS APPEARS VERY OLD FASHIONED AT FIRST GLANCE.
2. NO. I AM NOT ON AN ISLAND. I REPEAT I AM NOT ON AN ISLAND.
3. I MISS MIDTOWN MANHATTAN. I WISH I WERE THERE NOW.
4. THERE ARE A LOT OF ARMED GUARDS OUTSIDE. THEY ARE PATROLLING THE GRAVEYARD.
5. I'M GLAD THIS HQ IS NOT IN THE AIR. I'M SCARED OF HEIGHTS.
6. THERE IS NOT A LIVING SOUL AROUND FOR MILES, EVEN LATVERIA IS LIVELIER THAN THIS PLACE.

THE MISSING S.H.I.E.L.D. AGENT WAS LAST SEEN AT:

ANSWERS ON PAGE 61

BUSTING OUT

Tony Stark's prepping the Hulkbuster armour for battle! Help him make the final alterations to make sure his new suit's fully operational!

AHEAD OF THE GAME

Choose the helmet that matches the Hulkbuster:

A

B

C

CHARGED UP CHALLENGE

Tony needs to charge the Hulkbuster! Tick the cable that leads directly to his power core:

LIVE AND KICKING

Tony's building new legs for the Hulkbuster unit. Tick which piece of tech he won't need:

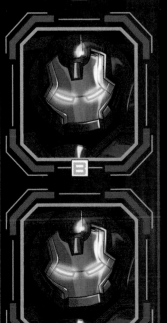

ANSWERS ON PAGE 61

45

1. MIXED MESSAGES!

S.H.I.E.L.D. is sending Spidey a scrambled police transmission about a robbery!

Put the phrases in the correct order to work out where the robbery is happening!

THE NATIONAL HISTORY MUSEUM

GET TO THE

MONUMENT BANK, IN-BETWEEN

AND SPARKLES' JEWELLERY STORE.

A ROBBERY IS OCCURRING NOW!

The place being robbed is:

2. CRIMINAL LINE-UP!

SUSPECT APPEARS TO BE MALE, IS NOT WEARING ANY BODY ARMOUR, DOES NOT HAVE AN ELONGATED TONGUE, DISPLAYS HUMAN SKIN IN THE FACE AND HAS NO FACIAL HAIR...

So we know where the robbery's happening, but who's the robber? Use the description from Spidey's Spider-Cycle to work it out!

ND GRAB!

HELP SPIDEY FOIL A ROBBERY BY SOLVING THE PUZZLES!

3. SPEEDY SPIDEY!

So that's who the robber is! Spidey will have to get there fast to stop him!

Find a route from start to finish that avoids all of the red lights!

FINISH

4. SCENE OF THE CRIME!

The robber has split himself into 10 piles of sand to hide from the police!

Circle all 10 of them in the crime scene below!

COMMS DISRUPTION

IRON MAN IS RECEIVING INCOMING MESSAGES. BUT THE SOUND CHANNELS ARE MIXED UP WITH THE SCREEN IMAGES. CAN YOU MATCH THE CORRECT WORDS WITH THE RIGHT SCREEN?

1 — **D**

THE FIRST ONE HAS BEEN DONE FOR YOU...

DIFFICULTY LEVEL: 1 2 3

2

3

4

5

6

7

A STOP HASSLING ME ALREADY! I'M FLYING AS FAST AS I CAN!

B ONE MAY CONSIDER ME A GOD, YES. BUT A FRIEND ALSO...

C MY ARROWS HAVE NO EFFECT ON IT, SO ERR, HELP?

D BAH! MY HYDRA AGENTS WILL TRACK YOU DOWN...

E REMEMBER ME STARK? YOUR FAVE RIVAL WEAPONS INVENTOR.

F WE HAVE COME TO CHALLENGE YOU SURFACE DWELLERS.

F THRUSTERS ARE DOWN 30% AND IT WON'T FLY IN A STRAIGHT LINE?!

ANSWERS ON PAGE 61

IT'S ALL RIGHT, SON. JUST A LITTLE TURBULENCE, THAT'S ALL.
UH...SORRY, LADIES AND GENTLEMEN, WE MUST'VE HIT A PATCH OF ROUGH AIR. JUST SIT TIGHT UNTIL WE TURN OFF THE "FASTEN SEATBELT" SIGN AND WE'LL BE A-OKAY IN A MINUTE.
SEE?
!
YES, HUMANS, YOU WILL BE FINE...BUT ONLY IF YOU PLAY A LITTLE GAME WITH ME.
THAT VOICE!
ONE OF YOU HAS SOMETHING THAT I WANT, AND UNLESS THAT SOMEONE COMES FORWARD IN THE NEXT SIXTY SECONDS--
"--I WILL DROP THIS VESSEL INTO THE OCEAN!"

5 THINGS YOU NEVER KNEW ABOUT...

ULTRON

1.

Ultron is a 6ft 9 monster in a practically indestructible adamantium shell, weighing a mighty 735 pounds!

2.

Ultron formed the Masters of Evil II, and led the team to try and defeat the Avengers.

3.

Ultron created the Vision using components from an android called the Human Torch.

4.

His aim is to conquer the world and wipe out all humankind... better watch your back.

5.

This terrifying android has upgraded himself more than 20 times!

6 LABYRINTH OF HONOUR

- START
- MUSPELHEIM
- HE SACRIFICED IT TO THE WELL OF MIMIR
- TRUE
- TRUE
- THE HEART OF A STAR
- FINISH

8 TRUE or FALSE!

| 1 | TRUE | 3 | FALSE | 5 | FALSE |
| 2 | FALSE | 4 | TRUE | 6 | FALSE |

22 STORM WARNING

1. MY VIBRANIUM SHIELD SHOULD PROTECT US FROM THOSE ATLANTEAN WEAPONS.
2. I CAN'T BELIEVE WE CRASHED ANOTHER AVENJET. THAT'S THE THIRD ONE THIS WEEK!
5. LUCKY FALCON ISN'T HERE. HIS WING SUIT WOULD GET BLOWN TO PIECES IN THIS STORM.
3. HULK SMASH PUNY ATLANTEANS!
4. EVEN MY MIGHTY HAMMER MJOLNIR CANNOT STOP RAN'S WINDS!

24 BANNER'S LAB

D.

START ... FINISH

26 INFINITY MAZE

38 TWICE BITTEN

40 SECRET BASES

THE MISSING S.H.I.E.L.D. AGENT WAS LAST SEEN AT:

Castle Dracula

44 FREEFALL

START — FINISH

45 BUSTING OUT

46 SMASH AND GRAB

1. GET TO THE MONUMENT BANK, IN-BETWEEN THE NATIONAL HISTORY MUSEUM AND SPARKLES' JEWELLERY STORE. A ROBBERY IS OCURRING NOW!

2. ✓

3. FINISH

4.

48 COMMS DISRUPTION

1	2	3	4	5	6	7
D	C	G	D	E	A	B